The Legend of Sleepy Hollow

For my children, who love spooky stories.

—J.M.

ISBN-13: 978-0-545-03333-6
ISBN-10: 0-545-03333-0

12 11 10 9 8 7 6 5   8 9 10 11 12/0

Printed in the U.S.A.
First printing, September 2007

Book design by Jennifer Rinaldi Windau

101 Words to Know

The Legend of Sleepy Hollow

by Washington Irving

Adapted by Joanne Mattern

SCHOLASTIC INC.
NEW YORK TORONTO LONDON AUCKLAND SYDNEY
MEXICO CITY NEW DELHI HONG KONG BUENOS AIRES

Get ready for 4th grade with

101 Words to Know

Learning vocabulary words by reading them

in context is the best way to retain their meaning.

Adapted from the original story for young readers, 101 words you

need to know by the 4th grade are in bold throughout the book.

Also on the page are the definitions of those words. No need to flip

back for definitions; no need to look them up in the dictionary. It's

easy to learn new

vocabulary words while reading

a timeless classic!

TABLE OF CONTENTS

Table of Contents

CHAPTER 1:
The Ghosts of Sleepy Hollow

Long ago, right after the Revolutionary War in the early 1800s, the village of Tarry Town lay right by the Hudson River in the Hudson Valley. There were hills and valleys and forests full of green trees. The silver waters of the Hudson River flowed through the valley, bringing life and beauty to the land. However, people believed that ghosts and goblins also roamed the land. Tarry Town was one of the most **terrifying** places in this beautiful area. These ghosts were not friendly! Instead, they loved to scare the people of the valley.

terrifying (adj.)—something scary

The men, women, and even children of Tarry Town thought about ghosts all the time. They talked about them. They shared stories of hauntings and scary meetings with the spirits. "Don't travel the roads around here at night," folks would whisper. "You never know what horrible creature you might meet!"

You might wonder why Tarry Town was such a spooky place. After all, you have probably never seen a ghost. Why were there so many spirits in Tarry Town? Tarry Town was a very old village. Farmers **settled** there and never moved away. Their families lived there as well. Things didn't change much as time passed. So when the

settle, **settled** (v.)—to establish a home in an area

ghosts came out of their graves, they found plenty of **familiar** places and people to haunt.

Of all the scary places in Tarry Town, none was more **frightening** than a spot called Sleepy Hollow. Sleepy Hollow was a lovely place. Tall trees grew in the woods. Thick grass **covered** the ground. In the spring and summer, the air was filled with the sweet smell of wildflowers in bloom. A bubbling stream flowed through Sleepy Hollow, making a merry noise along the rocks.

But if you thought Sleepy Hollow was a peaceful place, you would be wrong! **Underneath** the beauty lay a dark secret. If you **listened** carefully, you might hear

familiar (adj.)—easily recognized; everyday happening
frightening (adj.)—something that is scary
cover, **covered** (v.)—to put something over something else
underneath (prep.)—directly under; something covered or hidden
listen, **listened** (v.)—to pay attention so you can hear something

much more than the sound of the flowing stream. You might hear ghostly footsteps. You might hear a horse's hooves when there was no one around. Worst of all, you might hear horrible screams! Sleepy Hollow was haunted by many ghosts. And there was one ghost that was more terrifying than all the rest.

Chapter 2:
The Headless Horseman

Of all the ghosts that haunted Tarry Town, none was feared more than the Headless Horseman of Sleepy Hollow. This ghost **roamed** the roads at night and struck terror into the hearts of everyone. Why was this rider so scary? He had no head!

"I'll tell you the legend of the Headless Horseman," a farmer said one night as folks gathered around a fire. "The Horseman was a soldier. He fought for the British during the Revolutionary War. One day, during a battle, American soldiers fired their cannons. A shot

roam, **roamed** (v.)—to go from place to place without a purpose or direction

came right at the Horseman! Before he could duck, a cannonball blew his head clean off." The storyteller's voice dropped to a whisper. "The Horseman's head was never seen again." His listeners shivered with delight.

"The Horseman was buried in the village churchyard," the farmer went on, "but without his head he could not rest in peace. Instead, he rises from his grave every night. **Mounting** his horse, he races across the countryside to the site of the battle. There he searches **desperately** for his missing head." The farmer finished his tale, "When daylight comes, the Headless Horseman races back to his grave to rest until night

mount, **mounting** (v.)—to seat oneself upon a horse
desperately (adv.)—frantically

falls once more upon the village."

Many people claimed to have seen and heard the Headless Horseman. "I saw a huge figure whose cloak swept out behind him like the wings of a giant blackbird," someone said. Another spoke of the pounding hooves of his giant horse. "Those hooves created such a terrible noise that I was startled right out of my bed," he said.

"You know the Headless Horseman carries a pumpkin head wherever he goes," another storyteller added. "**Usually** the pumpkin rests on the front of his saddle. But if anyone gets in the Horseman's way, look

usually (adv.)—most of the time

out! He will throw that pumpkin right at you!"

At parties and other gatherings, guests talked about the Headless Horseman for hours. And if anyone had to go out after dark, he or she made as much noise as possible, trying to scare the Headless Horseman away. Only a fool would willingly cross paths with the frightening ghost. And nobody ever stepped out after midnight. Though they loved to tell his story, nobody wanted to meet him or his horrible horse.

CHAPTER 3:
Ichabod Crane

People who had lived in Tarry Town all their lives were always thinking about the Headless Horseman. But they were not the only ones who were **fascinated** by him. New townspeople soon heard the stories. They often became fascinated with the ghost as well.

Ichabod Crane was someone who came to Tarry Town and became **infected** with ghost fever. Ichabod was the village schoolmaster. He moved to Tarry Town from Connecticut. He had never heard stories like the ones told about Sleepy Hollow and the Headless Horseman!

fascinate, **fascinated** (v.)—to attract and hold someone's attention
infect, **infected** (v.)—to pollute; to contaminate

Ichabod Crane was a funny-looking man. His head was small, but his ears were huge. The strangest things about Ichabod were his arms and legs. They were incredibly long. It looked like Ichabod's hands hung a mile below his shirtsleeves. From a distance, Ichabod looked like a scarecrow that had walked out of a cornfield.

Ichabod came to Tarry Town to teach in the one-room schoolhouse which was right in the middle of spooky Sleepy Hollow. Ichabod was a **strict** teacher but people liked him. "Pay attention," he would scold. "Keep your eyes on your work." If students did not behave, Ichabod

strict (adj.)—extremely stern

was quick to take a long birch rod and strike them with it. But even though Ichabod was strict, his students liked him. He was fair and **patient**. He often played games with the older students and he spent a lot of time helping the younger ones with their lessons.

After school, Ichabod could usually be found lying under a tree. He always had a book in his hand. Usually, this book was filled with stories of witches and ghosts. Ichabod loved nothing more than a good ghost story!

At that time, teachers were much respected. But they did not make a lot of money. Ichabod's **salary** was not enough for him to **purchase** food and a house. Instead,

patient (adj.)—being calm
salary (n.)—money paid regularly for a service
purchase (v.)—to buy something

Ichabod lived with his students. Every week, a different family would host him. At the end of the week, Ichabod would move on to the next family.

There were a lot of jobs to do on the farms. Ichabod did his **best** to help every family he stayed with. He made hay and fixed fences. He **fetched** water and cut wood. He fed the horses and drove the cows into the barn. "That Ichabod certainly is a hard worker," everyone said.

Everyone also agreed that Ichabod loved to eat. Ichabod was skinny, but he ate as much as three men! Ichabod loved pudding and fresh-baked pies. He licked

best (adj.)—better than everything else
fetch, **fetched** (v.)—to go and get

his lips when he saw plump turkeys and tender hams. Sweet cakes and tarts were also favorite foods. The host family would stare in wonder as skinny Ichabod ate and ate! **However**, they didn't really mind. "Your cooking is the finest in the land," Ichabod would tell the household's mothers and daughters. He also charmed the pretty daughters by reading poetry to them. Many young men **envied** Ichabod because he told such good stories.

Of course, Ichabod's favorite stories were about ghosts. Many nights after dinner, Ichabod would visit other families in Sleepy Hollow. As the family gathered

however (conj.)—in spite of
envy, envied (v.)—to want what someone else has

close around the fire, Ichabod shared stories of ghosts and goblins. He got these stories from books and from other homes where he had stayed. In return, the families shared their own stories. They talked about haunted houses and barns. They spoke of spooky fields and bridges.

Soon someone would tell Ichabod's favorite ghost story—the story of the Headless Horseman. Ichabod would pull his chair closer to the fire. In spite of the warmth of the flames, chills would run down his spine. The storyteller's voice would rise spookily out of the near-darkness, making the story even more frightening. Ichabod's heart pounded with fear—and with delight!

Ichabod knew he was safe by the fire. But all too soon, it was time to go home. He had to walk home alone in the dark, and Ichabod was afraid. The woods were terrifying at night. He would tiptoe carefully through the trees. In the darkness, it was easy for his **imagination** to run wild. Every light was a ghost. Every sound was a goblin's footsteps. Every shadow was a horrible spirit come to grab him!

Most of all, Ichabod feared the Headless Horseman. One night, he got the greatest fright of his life. As he walked home through the thick darkness, he felt the ground shaking beneath his feet. In the distance, he heard the galloping hooves of a horse!

"Aah!" Ichabod screamed. He was filled with fear. He began to run. But it was hard to see the path in

imagination (n.) —creative ability

the darkness. The sound of the horse came closer and closer. Ichabod's heart pounded. Sweat poured down his body. The horse was almost on top of him!

Ichabod's foot caught on a tree root. He tripped and fell to the ground. *Surely this is the end!* he thought. Then the **frantic** schoolmaster heard the horse and its rider race past him. The noise and the horse **faded** away.

Ichabod **staggered** to his feet. He was **gasping** for breath. He was **sure** he had barely escaped the deadly hands of the Headless Horseman!

Ichabod made his way back to the farm where he was

---

frantic (adj.)—wildly excited or frightened
fade, **faded** (v.)—to go away or backward
stagger, **staggered** (v.)—to walk unsteadily
gasp, **gasping** (v.)—to pant loudly and with effort
sure (adj.)—having no doubt

staying. He was still trembling and breathing heavily

but he never mentioned his terrifying experience.

Chapter 4:
The Van Tassel Farm

Ichabod Crane was not only the schoolmaster. He **possessed** a fine singing voice and he often sang as he walked through the countryside. Since he had the **ability** to sing very well, he became the singing teacher. Every week, most of the children and teenagers of the village came to Ichabod's singing classes.

Ichabod was strict but fair as a schoolmaster and he treated his singing students the same way. If a student could not sing well, Ichabod did not **punish** him or her. "Try again," he would say. "Do your best." If a student

possess, possessed (v.)—to own
ability (n.)—the power to do something
punish (v.)—to deal with harshly

had a **talent** for singing, Ichabod made that student work harder. He wanted all of his students to be the best they could be.

But there was one student he could not control. That student was Katrina Van Tassel. No matter what Katrina did wrong, Ichabod did not criticize her.

Maybe the **problem** was that Katrina was very beautiful. Her blond hair hung in long curls. She had pale skin. She wore the latest fashions, and her jewelry was made of the finest gold.

Katrina's family was rich and she was an only child. Her parents spoiled her. Although she was sweet and

talent (n.)—a special ability to master something
problem (n.)—a difficult situation that needs to be solved

friendly, she was used to getting her way. Katrina had a beautiful singing voice but she did not practice her singing as much as she should. Instead of singing, she liked to flirt with the boys. If another student had done this, Ichabod would have shouted, "Pay attention! Stop your nonsense!" But he never got angry with Katrina. "Very nice, my dear," he would say, and he would let her do whatever she wanted.

The other students wondered about Ichabod's strange **behavior**. Their families wondered, too. Some people whispered, "Do you think Ichabod is in love with Katrina?"

behavior (n.)—the way in which someone acts

One day, Ichabod had to meet with Katrina's father, Baltus Van Tassel. He set out for the Van Tassel farm. He had never been there before.

Ichabod had stayed on many farms during his time in Tarry Town. These farms were comfortable, but they were not fancy. Ichabod thought that the Van Tassel farm would be the same way. He got a big surprise when he saw it!

The Van Tassel farm was located on the shores of the Hudson River. When he saw it, Ichabod could hardly believe his eyes. "What a wonderful place!" he gasped. **Vast** fields stretched in every direction. Every field was

vast (adj.)—huge

bursting with a different crop. Ichabod saw wheat, rye, and corn. Then he saw the orchards. The trees were heavy with apples, pears, and other fruit.

Ichabod **proceeded** toward the barn. "This is the largest barn I've ever seen in my life!" he said to himself. "Just look inside!" The building was full of animals. Fat pigs lay in their pens. A flock of turkeys gobbled in the yard. Nearby, a flock of chickens pecked at the ground. Ducks and geese swam in a nearby pond. Fine horses ran through the pasture. Ichabod **observed** a huge herd of cows in a nearby field. Another field held woolly white sheep.

burst, **bursting** (v.)—to overflow
proceeded (v.)—to go forward
observe, **observed** (v.)—to watch carefully

Ichabod's thoughts swam. In his mind all the animals were changed into **ingredients** for delicious dinners. Ichabod imagined plump pigs roasting over a fire, each one with a baked apple in its mouth. Ichabod pictured the ducks swimming in thick, brown gravy instead of water. He smelled fruit pies baking in the oven. Suddenly, Ichabod wanted to sit at the Van Tassel table and eat until he burst.

Ichabod hurried into the farmhouse. The house was grand. Ichabod walked **across** the front porch. It was big enough to hold a dinner party. Inside the house, Ichabod saw fine furniture. The dining room was filled

ingredient (n.)—one of the items something is made from
across (prep.)—from one side to the other

with **expensive** dishes. *If only all those plates and bowls were filled with food*, Ichabod thought dreamily.

The simple schoolmaster felt like he was in a wonderland. He had never seen such riches. The animals! The crops! The furniture! The buildings! It was all too much. A wave of greed swept over Ichabod. "I want everything in this house to belong to me," he said to himself. "And I know just how to get what I want. I have to marry Katrina Van Tassel!"

expensive (adj.)—something that costs a lot
volunteer, volunteered (v.)—to work without getting paid

CHAPTER 5:
Ichabod and Brom

Ichabod liked the idea of marrying Katrina. Katrina was a beautiful and charming young lady. She also liked Ichabod. He was different from the other young men in Tarry Town. The other young men were farmers or the sons of farmers. They were awkward and rough. They did not know much about the world.

Ichabod, on the other hand, had excellent manners. He had read many books. Even though Ichabod was not handsome, many young women enjoyed spending time with him. He was an important man in Tarry Town. However, Ichabod was only interested in one girl.

Ichabod began to visit Katrina at home. He **volunteered** to help Katrina with her singing lessons. The two sang together in the parlor. "You have such a lovely voice," Ichabod told her. "It is just like a bird singing."

Katrina would blush prettily. "Thank you, Ichabod," she whispered.

The two went for long walks around the farm. They sat near the river and talked for hours. Ichabod told funny stories that made Katrina laugh. He praised Katrina's beauty and charm. Katrina found all the attention very **agreeable**. Soon, Ichabod's visits became more **frequent**.

Katrina's parents did not mind Ichabod's visits. If Katrina wanted to spend time with the schoolmaster,

agreeable (adj.)—pleasing; likable
frequent (adj.)—often

that was fine with Mr. Van Tassel. Mrs. Van Tassel felt the same way.

There was just one person who minded that Ichabod was spending so much time with Katrina. That person was a Dutchman named Brom Bones. Brom Bones was the most popular young man in Tarry Town. He was also in love with Katrina Van Tassel!

Brom and Ichabod could not be more different from each other. Brom was very handsome. He was tall and strong. He had **broad** shoulders and long legs. His black hair was thick and curly. He was good at riding horses. Brom was also good at causing trouble. Brom was the

broad (adj.)—wide

strongest and most daring man in Tarry Town. He and his friends often played practical jokes on people. People often heard them yelling and laughing as they rode home late at night. However, everyone knew they were just having fun. No one really minded Brom's **mischief**. At least they *said* they didn't mind! No one was going to argue with Brom. They would just shake their heads and say, "Brom Bones again!"

Like Ichabod, Brom had his heart set on Katrina Van Tassel. He visited her many times. His horse, Daredevil, was often tied up in front of the Van Tassel barn. All of the other young men in Tarry Town knew they did not

mischief (n.)—playful behavior that may cause harm to others

have a chance of winning Katrina if Brom wanted her. However, Ichabod would not give up. It seemed that Katrina **encouraged** him to come see her.

Brom was **furious** that Katrina liked Ichabod more than she liked him. "How dare that skinny schoolmaster push his way into Katrina's heart!" he shouted to his friends. "How could she like him better than me?" No one dared answer him. He stopped visiting Katrina.

Ichabod knew that Brom wanted to fight him. He also knew that he could never win a fight **against** the strong young Dutchman. So he ignored Brom's insults. In fact, he stayed as far away from Brom as he could.

encourage, encouraged (v.)—to praise someone
furious (adj.)—very angry
against (prep.)—competing with

Brom came up with other ways to **threaten** the schoolmaster. He played many practical jokes on Ichabod. One night, Brom stopped up the chimney of the schoolhouse. When Ichabod lit the fire the next day, the room filled with smoke. Another night, Brom and his friends broke into the schoolhouse. They turned all the desks and chairs upside down. When Ichabod came to school the next morning, he could not believe his eyes. "Witches must have held a meeting right here in the schoolhouse!" he cried.

Brom also taught a stray dog to howl whenever Ichabod sang. Every time Ichabod opened his mouth,

threaten (v.)—to make someone feel they are in danger.

the dog howled and whined. The animal made so much noise that no one could hear a word Ichabod sang. Everyone laughed at the poor schoolmaster.

One night, Brom gave Ichabod a terrible scare. Ichabod was walking home through the woods. It was almost dark, and the air was filled with shadows. Ichabod looked around **nervously** as he walked. Suddenly, he heard a terrifying sound. It was the sound of a galloping horse!

Ichabod began to run. But he did not get very far. A huge black horse blocked his path. Seconds later, something flew through the air—right at Ichabod! A

nervously (adv.)—uneasy; troubled; tense

pumpkin smashed to the ground just a few inches from where Ichabod stood. The poor schoolmaster froze with terror. Surely he had just met the Headless Horseman!

Then Ichabod heard laughter. He knew that voice. It was Brom Bones! Brom and Daredevil were just trying to scare him. And their trick had worked.

Brom did not stop pulling tricks on Ichabod. His **mission** was to get the schoolmaster to leave Katrina alone. But Ichabod was determined to win Katrina and the Van Tassel farm. "I'll never give up, no matter what Brom does to me," Ichabod swore.

mission (n.)—a special job

Chapter 6:
An Exciting Invitation

One warm fall afternoon, Ichabod was in the schoolhouse. His students worked quietly at their seats. Ichabod sat at his desk and watched over the class. He held a birch rod. He had just used it to spank a student who was not paying attention. Ichabod's desk was covered with objects he had taken away from his students that day. Ichabod did not allow his students to play in class.

Suddenly, the quiet afternoon was **shattered** by pounding hooves. Everyone looked out the window. A man rode up to the schoolhouse and jumped down from

shatter, **shattered** (v.)—to break into many pieces

his horse. He was wearing servant's clothes. After he tied his horse to the railing, the servant knocked on the door to the schoolhouse. "Enter!" Ichabod called.

The man ran in and handed Ichabod a **formal** invitation. Then he ran outside and jumped back on his horse. It was clear he had many invitations to deliver that afternoon.

"Back to work!" Ichabod snapped at his **curious** students. They quickly looked down at their books. As soon as the room was quiet, Ichabod opened the note. It read, YOU ARE INVITED TO A PARTY AT THE VAN TASSEL ESTATE TONIGHT.

Ichabod smiled as he read the **request** again. A

formal (adj.)—proper; fancy; not casual
curious (adj.)—nosy
request (n.)—something that is asked for; invitation

party at the Van Tassel farm! Katrina would be there. Best of all, there would be plenty of food! This was an **opportunity** he could not miss.

There was no time to waste! Ichabod rushed his students through their lessons. "Hurry! Hurry!" he shouted. The **confused** students did not know what had come over their schoolmaster. "Put everything away!" Ichabod cried. "There is no time to waste!" Books were tossed aside instead of being put back on their shelves. Benches were knocked down and left there. Strangest of all, Ichabod said, "Now everyone go home!" School was let out an hour **early**. The children ran out of the

opportunity (n.)—a chance to do something
confused (adj.)—not able to understand
early (adv.)—before the usual time

schoolhouse, yelling and laughing with joy.

When the schoolhouse was finally empty, Ichabod got to work. He wanted to look his best for the **occasion**. The teacher stood in front of the broken mirror. He shaved and washed his face. Then he combed his thin hair until he was **satisfied** with the way it looked. Next, Ichabod put on the only suit he owned. The suit was old and black. He brushed his hands over the suit to clean it. Ichabod stood in front of the mirror and smiled at what it **reflected**. "What a fine sight I am!" he said. "Katrina will be very **impressed**!"

Ichabod wanted to look good when he arrived at the

occasion (n.)—an event; a time when something happens
satisfy, **satisfied** (v.)—to be content
reflect, **reflected** (v.)—to show an image of something on a shiny surface
impress, **impressed** (v.)—to make people think highly of someone

Van Tassel farm. He walked to the house where he was staying. "Mr. Van Ripper," he said to the farmer, "would you be so kind as to **lend** me your horse for tonight?"

"Yes, of course," said Hans Van Ripper. He gave Ichabod a horse named Gunpowder.

Gunpowder was an old, broken-down horse that had once pulled a plow. He was thin and bony. His mane and tail were tangled and knotted. A big head rested on the end of a skinny neck. Gunpowder was blind in one eye. His other eye had a nasty **gleam**. Even though Gunpowder was old, he was known to have a bit of the devil in him.

lend (v.)—to give something you expect back; to loan something
gleam (n.)—a small bright light; a flash

Ichabod and Gunpowder were a funny sight as they rode through Tarry Town. The stirrups on the saddle were too short. Ichabod had to ride with his bony knees sticking straight up by his face. His bony elbows stuck out like a grasshopper's legs. His arms flapped like a pair of wings. Ichabod's black coat fluttered out behind him. A hat was perched on his forehead, sliding over his eyes. Ichabod thought he looked grand.

But he did not hear people whispering and laughing behind his back. "What a wild man!" they said. "He looks like a crazy bird! Maybe he is trying to look like one of the spirits in those stories he tells." It was true. Ichabod and Gunpowder looked as strange as some of the ghosts that were said to wander Tarry Town at night!

CHAPTER 7:
A Fine Feast

Ichabod rode up the lane to the Van Tassel farm. He rode past orchards where apples hung heavily from the trees. Baskets overflowing with picked fruit sat on the ground.

Next, Ichabod passed vast fields of corn. The teacher imagined biting into the sweet, crunchy ears. Then Ichabod passed the pumpkin patch. He was delighted to see the big orange pumpkins lying in the sun. What fine pies they would make!

Ichabod smiled as he rode up to the barn. The air smelled sweet and fresh. The evening was warm. Best of all, he was going to see Katrina and eat the wonderful food her family had prepared for the party!

Ichabod climbed down from Gunpowder. He tied the

old horse to the fence in front of the barn. Many other horses were tied there already. One of these horses was Daredevil. However, Ichabod did not notice Brom's horse. Instead, he **hurried** to join the party.

The house was filled with people. Almost everyone in Tarry Town was there. Farmers wore their best coats and shoes with shiny buckles. The farmers' wives wore white caps and long dresses. Young girls, with ribbons in their long hair, ran by. Young men wore short coats lined with rows of shiny buttons.

Brom Bones was there. He was dressed in his best clothes. A group of young men and girls gathered

hurry, **hurried** (v.)—to go fast

around him. It was clear that Brom was the center of attention. Ichabod hurried past Brom without speaking. He had other things on his mind.

At last, Ichabod found what he was looking for. The dining room tables were covered with food! Silver platters were piled high with ham, smoked beef, and fresh fish. Other platters held roast turkeys, chickens, and ducks. Another table was filled with sweet desserts: doughnuts and crullers, sweet cakes, honey cakes, and ginger cakes. And then there were the pies! Ichabod saw apple, peach, pumpkin, and plum pies. There were jams and pudding, too. There were jugs of cider and bowls of cream and milk. A huge teapot sent clouds of steam into the air.

Ichabod had never seen so much fine food in his life. His mouth was watering and his stomach was growling.

"No time to waste," he said. "I must eat **promptly**!" The teacher grabbed chicken legs and ham slices. He piled his plate with plenty of everything. He only stopped for a moment when Baltus Van Tassel came up to greet him. Ichabod said hello with a turkey leg sticking out of his mouth. Then he turned back to the food. "Delicious!" he mumbled.

Finally, even Ichabod could not eat another bite. He patted his full stomach and smiled. Good food always made Ichabod happy. *Someday the Van Tassel fortune will be mine*, he thought. The thought made him even happier.

promptly (adv.)—quickly

Just then, Ichabod heard music in the front hall. "It's time for the dancing!" he said with delight. The teacher quickly hurried into the other room.

Ichabod was not only a fine singer, he was also a very good dancer. When he danced, his **awkwardness** disappeared. Ichabod moved gracefully around the room. He headed straight for Katrina. "Will you dance with me?" he asked. Of course, Katrina said yes.

The two made a perfect pair. Katrina smiled as Ichabod told her how beautiful she was. Every young man in the room stared at him with envy.

No one felt more envy than Brom Bones. He sat in a

awkwardness (n.)—clumsiness; not stylish

corner watching Ichabod and Katrina dance. His face was red with anger. "What a ridiculous couple they make," he muttered. "It is time that teacher learned a lesson!"

As Ichabod twirled Katrina around the dance floor, his smile grew bigger and bigger. *Surely this night can not get any better*, he thought.

In fact, it was about to get much worse.

CHAPTER 8:
Ghost Stories

After a while, Ichabod went back to the dining room. He ate a doughnut. Then he walked out to the porch and joined a group of farmers. The men were talking about the Revolutionary War, when they had fought against the British army.

It seemed that every man had a story to tell. "Once I fired at an enemy warship," a farmer said. "I only had a **flimsy** mud wall to hide behind. I would have captured the ship, but my gun jammed. I had to run for my life!"

flimsy (adj.)—weak and fragile

Another farmer told of the Battle of White Plains.
"I heard a musket ball whiz right past my head!" he
said. "So I raised my sword and knocked the ball away
with the base of it!" Everyone oohed and ahhed at
his **incredible** tale. Clearly, these men were the best
soldiers America had ever seen.

Soon, war stories changed to ghost stories. One man
told the story of a huge tree where a British spy had
been killed. Every night, a ghostly funeral procession
passed the old tree. The ghosts in the procession were
horrible to see. Their howls and wails chilled everyone
who heard them.

incredible (adj.)—hard to believe; amazing

A man told the story of the ghost of Raven Rock. The ghost was a woman in white who had died by the rock **during** a terrible snowstorm. Ever **since** then, her spirit had wandered the valley on cold winter nights. People said that you could hear her screams on the wind during a storm.

Soon, talk turned to the most frightening ghost of all—the Headless Horseman. "I hear he's been seen in the woods again," said one farmer.

"I've seen him with my own eyes," another man agreed. "I've seen his horse, too. It's tied to a tree in the Sleepy Hollow graveyard at night."

during (prep.)—within a certain time
since (conj.)—from the time that

"**Remember** what happened to old Brouwer?" asked another farmer. "He met the Headless Horseman one night by the bridge near the church. The Horseman pulled Brouwer onto his horse. They galloped together down the road. Then the Headless Horseman changed into a skeleton and he threw old Brouwer into the brook."

Everyone nodded their heads. They knew Brouwer's story very well. They also knew that the Headless Horseman would not cross over that bridge. If a person could **reach** the other side, he was safe.

Suddenly, laughter filled the air. Then a loud voice announced, "I beat the Headless Horseman at his own

remember (v.)—to recall or bring back to mind
reach (v.)—to get through to

game!" Everyone turned to see who had spoken such bold words. It was Brom Bones.

"I would have beaten him if he had played fair," Brom went on. "Daredevil and I were riding through the valley when I met the Headless Horseman. I dared him to a race. The winner would get a bowl of punch. The Horseman agreed and off we ran."

Ichabod leaned forward as Brom went on with his tale. "We raced down the path. We jumped over fences and fallen trees. We cut through forests and fields. The Headless Horseman and his ghost horse were no match for Daredevil and me," Brom **boasted**. "We were about

boast, boasted (v.)—to brag; to speak with pride

to win the race when we came to the bridge. We would have beaten that ghost. But just as we reached the bridge, the Horseman disappeared in a flash of fire."

Everyone sighed and whispered to each other when Brom finished his story. Ichabod **shivered** with fear.

Suddenly, people noticed how late it was. No one wanted to be on the road at midnight. No one wanted to meet the Headless Horseman!

It was time to leave. Everyone put on their hats and coats. They said good-bye to Baltus Van Tassel and thanked him for the wonderful party. Then the families got in their carriages and rode away.

shiver, **shivered** (v.)—to tremble and shake uncontrollably

CHAPTER 9:
Disappointment and Fear

Ichabod stayed behind after everyone had left. He wanted to speak with Katrina in **private**. While he waited for her, Ichabod whistled happily. He was sure that all his dreams would come **true** that night.

Finally, Katrina came inside. Ichabod sat close by her. He talked softly and sweetly in her ear. But Katrina did not smile. Her face was blank. Finally, she said something to Ichabod. All the color drained from his face. As soon as Katrina finished, Ichabod grabbed his coat and ran out of the house. He did not even stop to

private (adj.)—for one person's ears only; confidential
true (adj.)—accurate; not false

get anything to eat.

What did Katrina say to Ichabod? No one knows what their **quarrel** was about. But it was clear that her words were not what Ichabod wanted to hear. The evening had turned into a **disaster**.

Ichabod jumped on Gunpowder's back. He kicked the horse to get him moving. But Gunpowder had been sleeping and he refused to gallop. Instead, he plodded slowly down the road. Nothing Ichabod did could make the old horse move any faster.

As Ichabod rode along the path by the river, he was surrounded by blackness. The moon and stars had

quarrel (n.)—an argument
disaster (n.)—an event that causes great damage; something that turns out very wrong

disappeared. The schoolmaster was alone in the dark. "It is a dark night and I am in a dark mood!" he said to himself. Then he remembered the scary stories he had heard at the party that night and shivered with fear.

Suddenly, a huge white shape loomed out of the night. Ichabod gasped. It was the tree where the British spy had been killed. The tree's limbs twisted around like a skeleton's fingers. Ichabod began to whistle nervously. *What's that?* he thought. *Is the ghost whistling back at me? No, it is just the wind.*

Ichabod looked up and saw a white figure above him. *Is that a ghost? No*, he thought with relief. He **realized**

disappear, **disappeared** (v.)—to go away suddenly; vanish
realize, **realized** (v.)—to understand; to know

that it was just a place where the tree had been struck by lightning.

Groans filled the night. Ichabod thought of the funeral procession. "Silly me!" he said nervously. "It is just two tree branches rubbing together."

Ichabod shivered as Gunpowder walked past the tree. He was safe. But his ride home was far from over.

Chapter 10:
Spirits in the Night

After he passed the tree, Ichabod saw the brook up ahead. The brook ran under a bridge built of logs. Then the water flowed into a swamp. The **area** around the bridge was overgrown with bushes and vines. It was a gloomy, scary place. Even in daylight, people did not like to go near the spot. At night, it was even more frightening.

Ichabod had no choice but to cross the bridge. He kicked Gunpowder's sides, hoping the horse would go faster. Instead, the horse changed direction! He **plunged**

area (n.)—part of a place
plunge, plunged (n.)—to dive into water or rush into something

into a thorny bush. Ichabod had to pull his horse out of the bush. He was covered in prickly leaves and thorns. But the schoolmaster didn't care. All he wanted was to get across the bridge.

Ichabod kicked Gunpowder again. The horse ran forward. But when he reached the bridge, he stopped so quickly that Ichabod almost flew right over his head. Angrily, Ichabod started to kick the horse again. But Gunpowder refused to **budge**.

Suddenly, Ichabod heard branches snapping behind him. He turned around. His face was white with fear. Gunpowder's ears folded back in fright.

budge (v.)—to move

A huge figure stood in the shadows behind Ichabod. It was dark and **misshapen**. It towered over the schoolmaster and his horse like a monster. The figure didn't move. It seemed to be waiting for Ichabod to do something.

The schoolmaster didn't know what to do. He could not turn around and go past the horrible figure. But he knew Gunpowder could never outrun the figure, either. His only chance was to cross the bridge. Could he and Gunpowder make it?

"Who are you?" Ichabod **inquired** of the strange figure. The creature did not answer. "Who are you,

---

misshapen (adj.)—wrongly shaped
inquire, inquired (v.)—to ask

I say?" Ichabod yelled. Again, his only answer was silence. Ichabod was more afraid than ever. He started to whistle a church tune.

Suddenly, the figure moved out of the shadows. It stood in the middle of the road. In the pale moonlight, Ichabod could not see the figure very well. He just knew it was a man of **massive** size, riding a big, black horse. Ichabod could not see the horseman's face.

Ichabod did not want to see anything more. "Move, Gunpowder!" he begged. The teacher kicked Gunpowder, trying to get the horse to move faster. For once, the horse obeyed. But the horseman moved,

massive (adj.)—huge

too. He followed right behind Ichabod.

Ichabod's mouth was so dry, he could not whistle anymore. He was shaking from head to toe. He felt Gunpowder's muscles tighten with fear as well. Could they **escape** this mysterious figure?

Once again, Ichabod looked back. For a moment, he **glimpsed** the creature against the sky. Ichabod could not believe his eyes. This horseman had no head! Instead, a pumpkin head rested on the front of his saddle. Ichabod's fear **increased**. Finally, he realized that he was face-to-face with the Headless Horseman of Sleepy Hollow!

escape (v.)—to get away
glimpse, **glimpsed** (v.)—to take a quick look
increase, **increased** (v.)—to grow in size or amount

Chapter 11:
Ichabod's Last Ride

Ichabod was terrified. He grabbed the reins and kicked Gunpowder as hard as he could. He had to get the horse across the bridge! Gunpowder knew that Ichabod was not fooling around. He galloped straight for the bridge.

Ichabod had never ridden so fast in his life. But it was not fast enough. The Headless Horseman had no trouble keeping up. Ichabod could hear the ghostly horse right behind him. Stones flew from under the horses' feet as they raced down the road.

The schoolmaster leaned forward. "Faster, Gunpowder!" he begged. "You have to go faster!" The horse did his best. Would it be enough? Would they reach the bridge before the Headless Horseman got them?

Suddenly, Gunpowder's saddle slid out from under Ichabod. The strap holding it to the horse broke. The saddle fell off and crashed to the ground. Ichabod **seized** Gunpowder's neck to stay on.

"Maybe the saddle will slow down the Headless Horseman," Ichabod said to himself. He turned back to look. What he saw scared him even more. The ghostly horse leaped over the saddle without slowing down at all.

Ichabod looked up again. The bridge was right in front of them. The schoolmaster remembered the stories he had heard at the party that night. If he could just get across that bridge, he would be safe!

seize, **seized** (v.)—to grab

"Come on, Gunpowder!" Ichabod yelled. "Just cross that bridge!"

Ichabod could feel the Headless Horseman's hot breath on his back. Steam rose from the ghost horse's nose. Then he heard Gunpowder's hooves clatter on the wooden bridge. Seconds later, they were across it. Ichabod yelled in **triumph**. Then he twisted around. Would the Headless Horseman disappear in a flash of smoke and light?

No! Instead, the Horseman stood up in his stirrups. He picked up the pumpkin head from the saddle in front of him. Then he **launched** it right at Ichabod.

triumph (n.)—a great victory
launch, **launched** (v.)—to send something into the air

The pumpkin flew through the air with amazing speed. Ichabod tried to duck, but it was too late. The pumpkin hit the schoolmaster in the back of the head. Ichabod was knocked right off his horse. He hit the ground and lay still. Gunpowder ran away in fright. Then the Headless Horseman galloped over the wall and disappeared into the graveyard.

Chapter 12:
A Mystery

The next morning, Hans Van Ripper found Gunpowder wandering through a field. His eyes looked **glazed** and they were twitching. His saddle was gone. And even though it was a warm day, Gunpowder could not stop shivering.

Van Ripper put out breakfast for Ichabod. But the schoolmaster never showed up. He did not come home for lunch or supper, either.

Ichabod was not at school. When the children realized that they had no teacher, they all went home.

glaze, **glazed** (v.) — to cover with a glassy film
despite (prep.) — in spite of
exploration (n.) — search

Their parents got worried when they heard that Ichabod had not shown up at school. They left their work behind to look for him.

It did not take long before the people of Tarry Town found some clues. "Look! I've found Gunpowder's saddle," one man called. "Here are two sets of horse's hooves," said another. Everyone could see that one set belonged to Gunpowder. The other disappeared into the graveyard.

"What's this?" called one of the children. "It's Ichabod's hat!" Everyone stared at the hat, which was lying next to the brook. Next to it was a shattered pumpkin.

"Search the brook!" a farmer cried. The people of Tarry Town searched the brook. They searched the woods, too. But the body of Ichabod Crane was never found, **despite** all these **explorations**. The schoolmaster was never seen again.

What happened to Ichabod Crane? The village was filled with stories. "I think Ichabod was so scared, he ran away from Tarry Town forever," said a young man. "He was just too afraid of Brom Bones," agreed another man. A woman had a different idea. "His heart was broken by whatever Katrina Van Tassel said to him," she said.

"Ridiculous!" some other people said. They had **opinions,** too. "Ichabod moved to New York City to become a successful politician."

But most people agreed with this **explanation**: "Ichabod Crane was carried away by the Headless

opinion (n.)—how a person feels about something
explanation (n.)—a reason for something

Horseman," they whispered.

Many people believed that Brom Bones knew what had happened that ghostly night. Brom laughed whenever he heard people talking about Ichabod Crane and the Headless Horseman. And it was true that soon after Ichabod disappeared, Brom Bones and Katrina Van Tassel got married. It all seemed very **suspicious**.

In time, the people of Tarry Town hired a new schoolmaster. They built a new schoolhouse, too. The old schoolhouse was **neglected** and **abandoned**. No one would go near it. It was haunted. Sometimes, late

---

suspicious (adj.)—thinking something is wrong
neglect, **neglected** (v.)—to not take care of something
abandon, **abandoned** (v.)—to leave or give up forever

at night, people said they heard a voice inside the building. That voice sang an old church tune. It was believed to be the ghostly voice of Ichabod Crane.

PUZZLES

Puzzles

Ghostly Jumble

Unscramble these letters to find words from the story.

IMLFRAIA

TTIRSC

ESICFIMH

REFITYR

ALEGM

NFIARCT

Sleepy Hollow Secret Code

Use the code below to figure out the secret message.
Substitute the correct letter for each number in the puzzle.
You'll come up with an important question about the story.

CODE:

A=26	G=20	M=14	S=19	Y=13
B=1	H=7	N=25	T=6	Z=12
C=24	I=18	O=23	U=17	
D=3	J=9	P=2	V=8	
E=22	K=16	Q=21	W=15	
F=5	L=11	R=4	X=10	

18 19   1 4 23 14   1 23 25 22 19   6 7 22

7 22 26 3 11 22 19 19   7 23 4 19 22 14 26 25 ?

Ichabod's Journey

Can you help Ichabod cross the bridge? Cross out the first
letter. Then cross out every second letter after that.
The remaining letters will spell out the type
of story *The Legend of Sleepy Hollow* is.

X G R H Y O E S W T P S Q T A O G R D Y

Crossword Clues

Use the vocabulary words in the box to finish each sentence.
Then write the answers in the puzzle.

**farm fascinated furious impress
quarrel terrify roamed**

ACROSS:

1. Ichabod Crane was _____ by ghost stories.

4. Brom Bones was _____ when Katrina paid
   attention to Ichabod.

5. Ghosts and goblins _____ the land.

6. Nothing could _____ Ichabod more than the
   story of the Headless Horseman.

DOWN:

1. Katrina Van Tassel lived on a huge _____.

2. Ichabod wanted to _____ Katrina at the party.

3. Katrina and Ichabod had a _____ at the end of
   the party.

Wild Ride Word Search

Can you find these words from the story in the puzzle?
Look across, up, down, backward, and diagonally.

across	music	broad	confuse	plunge	voice
encourage	problem	frantic	seize	hours	vast	listen

```
A  P  R  O  B  L  E  M  B  Q
M  G  T  N  S  E  D  N  E  L
U  R  A  F  B  E  N  E  D  R
S  I  O  R  G  S  I  C  H  V
I  T  S  A  V  E  P  Z  O  L
C  K  L  N  P  E  U  A  E  I
J  Q  U  T  L  H  O  U  R  S
E  C  Z  I  R  U  M  H  R  T
N  P  X  C  I  V  W  Z  A  E
C  O  N  F  U  S  E  B  D  N
O  H  S  E  I  A  S  A  H  Z
U  Z  S  U  A  D  O  X  S  Y
R  H  O  T  N  R  H  W  N  L
A  D  R  C  B  Y  M  Q  U  W
G  F  C  E  V  O  I  C  E  B
E  R  A  S  P  L  U  N  G  E
```

Scrambled Stories

Use the words in the box to fill in the missing word in each sentence. Then unscramble the circled letters to find a secret word that describes this book.

> **sang   volunteered   opportunity   pumpkin**
> **Gunpowder   black   Katrina   Daredevil   bridge**
> **feast   Baltus   river**

This story takes place on the banks of the Hudson __ __ _(_)_.

Ichabod was in love with __ _(_)_ __ __ __.

Katrina's father's name was _(_)_ __ __ __.

Ichabod took every __ __ __ _(_)_ __ __ __ __

to be with Katrina.

He __ __ _(_)_ __ __ __ __ __ __ to give her singing lessons.

Brom Bones had a horse named __ __ __ __ __ __ __ _(_)_.

Brom trained a dog to howl whenever Ichabod __ _(_)_ __.

Ichabod wanted to __ __ _(_)_ __ on food at the party.

Ichabod rode a horse named _(_)_ __ __ __ __ __ __.

The Headless Horseman rode a __ _(_)_ __ __ horse.

The Horseman chased Ichabod across the _(_)_ __ __ __.

He threw a __ __ _(_)_ __ __ at Ichabod's head.

The secret word is __ __ __ __ __ __ __ __ __ __ __ __ __.

83

I'm Not Scared of the Headless Horseman!

We're looking for words that mean the opposite—antonyms!
Fill in the blanks with words from the story.

> **broad   incredible   flimsy   punish   private**
> **vast   terrify   budge   disappear   neglected**

Forts are strong but a mud wall is _____.

If Ichabod Crane's shoulders were narrow,
Brom Bones's shoulders were _____.

Why comfort a person, if it is more fun to _____ them!

Van Tassel's fields were _____ while other farms were small.

Tales from battles were often _____ but the
real story was usually unremarkable.

Ichabod would _____ students but he also rewarded them.

Ichabod and Katrina talked in _____ but
their meetings became public knowledge.

Ichabod cared for the schoolhouse but when
he went away it was _____.

When the Headless Horseman appeared,
Ichabod wished it would _____.

Ichabod couldn't make Gunpowder _____ but
the Headless Horseman could.

Sleepy Hollow Word Chain

Ichabod was not only the school teacher.
Find what else he could do in the Word Chain puzzle. The
letters are in a chain—they may be next to each other
horizontally, vertically, or diagonally.

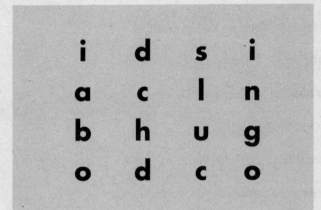

Vocabulary Words

noun (n.), verb (v.), adverb (adv.), adjective (adj.)

preposition (prep.), conjunction (conj.)

abandoned, **abandoned** (v.)—to leave or give up forever

ability (n.)—the power to do something

across (prep.)—from one side to the other

against (prep.)—competing with

agreeable (adj.)—pleasing; likable

area (n.)—part of a place

awkwardness (n.)—clumsiness; not stylish

behavior (n.)—the way in which someone acts

best (adj.)—better than everything else

boast, **boasted** (v.)—to brag; to speak with pride

broad (adj.)—wide

budge (v.)—to move

burst, **bursting** (v.)—to overflow

confused (adj.)—not able to understand

cover, **covered** (v.)—to put something over something else

curious (adj.)—nosy

desperately (adv.)—frantically

despite (prep.)—in spite of

disappear, **disappeared** (v.)—to go away suddenly; vanish

disaster (n.)—an event that causes great damage; something that turns out very wrong

during (prep.)—within a certain time

early (adv.)—before the usual time

encourage (v.)—to praise someone

envy, **envied** (v.)—to want what someone else has

escape (v.)—to get away

expensive (adj.)—something that costs a lot

explanation (n.)—a reason for something

exploration (n.)—search

fade, **faded** (v.)—to go away or backward

familiar (adj.)—easily recognized; everyday happening

fascinate, **fascinated** (v.)—to attract and hold someone's attention

fetch, fetched (v.)—to go and get

flimsy (adj.)—weak and fragile

formal (adj.)—proper; fancy; not casual

frantic (adj.)—wildly excited or frightened

frequent (adj.)—often

frightening (adj.)—something that is scary

furious (adj.)—very angry

gasp, gasping (v.)—to pant loudly and with effort

glaze, glazed (v.)—cover with a glassy film

gleam (n.)—a small bright light; a flash

glimpse, glimpsed (v.)—to take a quick look

however (conj.)—in spite of

hurry, hurried (v.)—to go fast

imagination (n.)—creative ability

impress (v.)—to make people think highly of someone

increase, increased (v.)—to grow in size or amount

incredible (adj.)—hard to believe; amazing

infect, infected (v.)—to pollute; to contaminate

ingredient (n.)—one of the items something is made from

inquire, **inquired** (v.)—to ask

launch, **launched** (v.)—to send something into the air

lend (v.)—to give something you expect back; to loan something

listen (v.)—to pay attention so you can hear something

massive (adj.)—huge

mischief (n.)—playful behavior that may cause harm to others

misshapen (adj.)—wrongly shaped

mission (n.)—a special job

mount, **mounting** (v.)—to seat oneself upon a horse

neglect, **neglected** (v.)—to not take care of something

nervously (adv.)—uneasy; troubled; tense

observe, **observed** (v.)—to watch carefully

occasion (n.)—an event; a time when something happens

opinion (n.)—how a person feels about something

opportunity (n.)—a chance to do something

patient (adj.)—being calm

plunge, **plunged** (n.)—to dive into water; to rush into something

possess, **possessed** (v.)—to own

private (adj.)—for one person's ears only; confidential

problem (n.)—a difficult situation that needs to be solved

proceed, **proceeded** (v.)—to go forward

promptly (adv.)—quickly

punish (v.)—to deal with harshly

purchase (v.)—to buy something

quarrel (n.)—an argument

reach (v.)—to get through

realize, **realized** (v.)—to understand; to know

reflect (v.)—to show an image of something on a shiny surface

remember (v.)—to recall or bring back to mind

request (n.)—something that is asked for; an invitation

roam, **roamed** (v.)—to go from place to place without a purpose or direction

salary (n.)—money paid regularly for a service

satisfy, **satisfied** (v.)—to be content

seize, **seized** (v.)—to grab

settle, **settled** (v.)—to establish a home in an area

shatter, **shattered** (v.)—to break into many pieces

shiver, **shivered** (v.)—to tremble and shake uncontrollably

since (conj.)—from the time that

stagger, **staggered** (v.)—to walk unsteadily

strict (adj.)—extremely stern

sure (adj.)—having no doubt

suspicious (adj.)—thinking something is wrong

talent (n.)—a special ability to master something

terrifying (adj,)—something scary

threaten (v.)—to make someone feel they are in danger

triumph (n.)—a great victory

true (adj.)—accurate; not false

underneath (prep.)—directly under; something covered or hidden

usually (adv.)—most of the time

vast (adj.)—huge

volunteer, **volunteered** (v.)—to work without getting paid

Puzzle Answers:

Ghostly Jumble

FAMILIAR

STRICT

MISCHIEF

TERRIFY

GLEAM

FRANTIC

Sleepy Hollow Secret Code

IS BROM BONES THE
HEADLESS HORSEMAN?

Ichabod's Journey

GHOST STORY

Crossword Clues

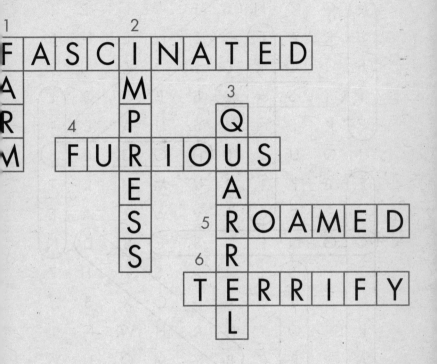

Wild Ride Word Search

```
A  P  R  O  B  L  E  M   B  Q
M  G  T  N  S  E  D  N  E  L
U  R  A  F  B  E  N  E  D  R
S  I  O  R  G  S  I  C  H  V
I  T  S  A  V  E  P  Z  O  L
C  K  L  N  P  E  U  A  E  I
J  Q  U  T  L  H  O  U  R  S
E  C  Z  I  R  U  M  H  R  T
N  P  X  C  I  V  W  Z  A  E
C  O  N  F  U  S  E  B  D  N
O  H  S  E  I  A  S  A  H  Z
U  Z  S  U  A  D  O  X  S  Y
R  H  O  T  N  R  H  W  N  L
A  D  R  C  B  Y  M  Q  U  W
G  F  C  E  V  O  I  C  E  B
E  R  A  S  P  L  U  N  G  E
```

Scrambled Stories

This story takes place on the banks of the Hudson R I V(E)R.

Ichabod was in love with K A(T)R I N A.

Katrina's father's name was B(A)L T U S.

Ichabod took every O P P O(R)T U N I T Y to be with Katrina.

He V O L(U)N T E E R E D to give her singing lessons.

Brom Bones had a horse named D A R E D E V I(L).

Brom trained a dog to howl whenever Ichabod S A(N)G.

Ichabod wanted to F E A(S)T on food at the party.

Ichabod rode a horse named G(U)N P O W D E R.

The Headless Horseman rode a B L(A)C K horse.

The Horseman chased Ichabod across the B(R)I D G E.

He threw a P U M(P)K I N at Ichabod's head.

The secret word is S U P E R N A T U R A L.

I'm Not Scared of the Headless Horseman!

Forts are strong but a mud wall is FLIMSY.

If Ichabod Crane's shoulders were narrow, Brom Bones's shoulders were BROAD.

Why comfort a person, if it is more fun to TERRIFY them!

Van Tassel's fields were VAST while other farms were small.

Tales from battles were often INCREDIBLE but the real story was usually unremarkable.

Ichabod would PUNISH students but he also rewarded them.

Ichabod and Katrina talked in PRIVATE but their meetings became public knowledge.

Ichabod cared for the schoolhouse but when he went away it was NEGLECTED.

When the Headless Horseman appeared, Ichabod wished it would DISAPPEAR.

Ichabod couldn't make Gunpowder BUDGE but the Headless Horseman could.

Sleepy Hollow Word Chain

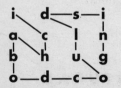

Ichabod could sing!